Magic Moments

Magic Moments

Donald Zolan Story Book

Paintings by
Donald Zolan

Editing by
Dolly Dickinson

Pemberton & Oakes Galleries, Ltd., Santa Barbara, California

First Edition

Library of Congress Cataloging in Publication Data

Zolan, Donald, 1937-
Magic Moments.

1. Zolan, Donald, 1937- —Juvenile literature.
2. Children in art—Juvenile literature. [1. Zolan,
Donald, 1937- . 2. Children in art. 3. Art
appreciation] I. Dickinson, Dolly. II. Title.
ND237.Z56A4 1988 759.13 88-28961
ISBN 0-9613070-2-1

Dedicated to
my daughters,
Sheila and Rhonda
—Dolly Dickinson

My New Kitten

Have you ever seen a kitten?
Have you touched its fluffy fur?
Have you ever held one in your arms
And heard its tiny purr?
Here's my little kitten.
It's coming to me now.
Soon it may even give me
A very small meow.
I'm being very patient
To help it feel at home.
I want it to be friends with me
And never, never roam.
Its ears are pointed forward
And its tail is in the air.
I'll always give my kitten
The tenderest of care.
I'll play with it and snuggle it
And pet and feed it too.
I'll hold it in my arms at night
And say, "I do love you."

Zolan.

Baby and Me

Here's my baby brother.
I love him very much.
He's wonderful to tickle.
He's wonderful to touch.
He loves to sit right in my lap
And rub against my nose.
I help him with his baby bath
And wash his baby toes.
We love to laugh together.
We giggle and we grin.
I'm such a lucky little girl
To get to be with him.
He has a happy, shining face
That's always full of joy.
I love to hold him close to me.
He's such a special boy.
Mother puts him on my lap
I hold him very tight.
I'll give him sixty kisses now
And an extra one tonight.

Zolan

My Bunny

I have a little bunny.
He's friendly as can be.
When I bend down to him,
He comes and nuzzles me.
He has a pink and wiggly nose
And long and floppy ears.
He perks them up like anything
At every sound he hears.
He's gentle and he's quiet
And he's white from head to toe.
He follows me with little hops
Every place I go.
When I get seated in the grass
He hops into my lap.
One day he got so tired he took
A little bunny nap.
I really love my bunny
And I tell him every day.
That's why my little bunny
Always comes to me to play.

Zolan

Baby Bath

Rub-a-dub-dub, I'm in my tub,
With bubbles everywhere.
They're on my hands, they're on my face,
They're even in my hair.
Such shiny bubbles! And what a day!
The sun is big and bright.
I'm just as warm inside my tub
As I am in bed at night.
My water won't sit still at all,
It sloshes all around,
And if I make a wave too big,
It splashes on the ground.
It's fun to splash and laugh and play
And watch my bubbles pop.
It's so much fun to be all wet
That I'm not going to stop.
I can't play with my brother now.
I think he went to school.
So I'll just stay and make-believe
This is my swimming pool.

Zolan

Almost Home

See my pup? He's on my back.
We've been a long, long way.
I really can't remember
All we did and saw today.
A big cow even mooed at us.
And then we turned around
Because my puppy hurt his paw
And lay down on the ground.
And so I put him in my bag.
I'm giving him a ride.
I think he's very happy there.
His eyes are big and wide.
Do you suppose he's thirsty now
And maybe hungry too?
Don't worry, pup. We're nearly home
And I'm right here with you.
We'll have some milk and cookies soon
And somewhere nice to rest.
Of all the things we've done today
I think this is the best.
You and I go everywhere.
We really like to roam.
But we both love it afterwards
When we are almost home.

Zolan.

Laurie's Christmas

It's finally Christmas morning,
I've waited for a year.
I got up very early
And hurried right down here.
I didn't eat my breakfast,
I didn't change my clothes.
I didn't put my slippers on
So you can see my toes.
I have this great big present,
It wiggles on my knees.
I pull the bow and hold on tight.
Will you help me, please?
I wonder what's inside the box?
It could be anything:
A book or dress or baby doll
That I can teach to sing.
See the ribbon in my hair?
It's satiny and white.
I think I may have 20 bows
To wear by Christmas night.

Zolan.

My Secret Creek

I got my net one morning
And went down to my creek.
Some minnows in the water
Were playing hide-and-seek.
One swam right in my net
And let me look at him.
I put him back and told him
To take another swim.
A deer came down to see me
Or maybe just to drink.
Just why he stayed so long
I really couldn't think.
Two little bugs were fighting;
I told them to behave.
A pretty duck came swimming by
And didn't make a wave.
A tiny caterpillar
Crawled right on my hand.
A robin made some funny chirps
I couldn't understand.
I have a lot of friends here.
I visit them a lot.
I'd tell you how to get here,
But it's my secret spot.

Erik and Dandelion

I wandered out alone today
To sit upon this hill.
I had a lot to think about.
I wanted to be still.
Everything around me
Was quiet as could be.
I had the hill all to myself
As far as I could see.
Then I picked a dandelion
That was soft and round.
I took it gently by its stem
And pulled it from the ground.
I made a wish and blew it hard
To see the seed pods fly.
Then as the seed pods floated off
I whispered a goodbye.
I watched them bob along on air.
I tried to count each one.
They looked like little silken threads
Dancing in the sun.
Where will they land? What will they do
When they are far away?
I'll come back here and think these thoughts
Again another day.

Zolan.

The Hideaway Turtle

Have you ever seen a turtle
Go inside its secret shell?
They're scaredy-cats and quick to hide,
They do it oh so well.
A turtle's house is like a rock.
It's very safe inside.
If you creep up to a turtle,
You may see the turtle hide.
This little girl is curious
To know what turtles do.
What do they eat? Where do they sleep?
And will they play with you?
The turtle sees the little girl.
She's peeking at it too.
Right away they both may say,
"How do you, do you do?"
They may turn into special friends
And share this summer day.
And then the girl may follow
When the turtle crawls away.

Zolan

Touching the Sky

It rained and it rained that wet summer day.
When it let up at last I ran out to play.
There were all kinds of puddles all over the place.
I looked down in one and I saw my own face.
In another a couple of clouds caught my eye.
I touched them and thought I was touching the sky.
I picked up a leaf and I made it a boat.
I was ever so happy it knew how to float.
Some puddles were little and some were like seas.
A bird was just starting to sing in the trees.
A long worm was squirming to get on dry ground.
I helped him because no one else was around —
Not a dog, not a cat, not even a car.
The air was so clear I could really see far.
Sometimes I wish it would rain every day.
After it stops, it's so much fun to play.

Zolan.

Daddy's Home

I've been watching out the window
Waiting for my Dad.
When he gets back from working,
Oh, will he be glad.

We've been baking chocolate cupcakes,
Frosting them with white,
Then topping them with candles
That my Dad will light.

Does he know we have surprises,
Birthday games to play?
Will he guess that we've been planning
Special things all day?

I keep looking out the window,
Watching so I'll see
When he drives into the driveway
Coming home to me.

Zolan

Grandma's Garden

I love my Grandma's garden
And everything that's there —
Bees and birds and butterflies
And flowers everywhere.
I'm sniffing at a flower,
One that's big and red.
I don't think I will pick it.
I'll leave it here instead.
It's redder than an apple.
It's red as it could be.
It may just be the reddest flower
I'm ever going to see.
And, oh, does it smell wonderful!
I really love its smell.
So maybe I'll just stand here
And really smell it well.
I love to play exciting games.
I love to jump and run.
But in my Grandma's garden
Smelling flowers is fun.

Zolan

Waiting for Santa

My little fuzzy poodle,
Don't bark on the step.
Don't you know we mustn't talk?
You cannot bark, not yet!
We're waiting here for Santa,
We mustn't say a word.
We're listening for reindeer.
What was that I heard?
Are those reindeer on the roof,
Is Santa coming near?
Quiet now, my little friend,
Santa's almost here.
Will he find us on the step
Hiding out of sight?
Oh, my little poodle,
This is such a special night.
Will you bark at Santa
When you see his bag of toys?
Are those pretty packages
For Santa's girls and boys?
Maybe if you're quiet,
He'll have a gift for you.
It may be a biscuit or a
Tasty bone to chew.

ZOLAN.

The Sea Shell

One day last summer I found a shell
Quite hidden in the sand.
I picked it up. It was big and white
And shining in my hand.

I put it to my ear and heard
Some waves, or maybe whales,
Or maybe mermaids singing
As they do in fairy tales.

Then suddenly I came to think
Of something fun to do.
I got my bucket and sat down
Into the water blue.

Now I can fill this pretty shell
And pour the water out
As fast or slow as I might wish —
It has a perfect spout!

Making Friends

Here's my new friend
My own pup.
He looks at me,
He says, "What's up?"
We're in the grass.
I'm on my knees.
My pup is saying,
"Play with me, please."
We're face to face
And nose to nose.
Now what next?
Well, I suppose
I'll chase him,
He'll chase me.
We have all day,
We're feeling free.
I'll throw him balls,
I'll throw him sticks.
I'll teach him new
And clever tricks.
When day is done
And dusk is here
He'll sleep close by
He's always near.
We're with each other
Day and night
We never leave
Each other's sight.

zolan.

My Reading Tree

I have a very special place
A very favorite tree
Where I can be all by myself
Though I'm not even three.

I like to sit between two roots
And see the clouds go by
And listen to the singing birds
Or watch a butterfly.

But best of all I like my tree
When I am reading there
Because the stories in my books
Can take me anywhere:

To circuses and zoos and trains
And castles far away;
On roller coasters, pirate ships,
Or right on Santa's sleigh.

Whenever I read by my tree
It's easy to pretend
Because each book's a magic place,
And each one is my friend.

On the Train

We're on the train, we're on our way,
We're rolling down the track,
And all the time here's what we hear:
Clickety-clickety-clack!
The whistle toots, the engine roars,
We're racing the sun to the West.
Of all the ways to travel far,
We love the train the best.
We're even wearing special caps
And sharing soda pop.
We're going faster than a car.
How will we ever stop?
Towns and farms are flying by.
It's like a picture show.
Here we go across a bridge
And there's a stream below.
Who'll be meeting us today?
Grandma and Grandpa too.
We'll run right in their arms and say,
"We both love seeing you!"

Beach Break

We're at the beach. It's summer time.
There's sand and sea and sun.
This fountain? It's a little tall,
So why not have some fun?
I'll be your ladder first and then
You be the same for me.
We won't take long because we know
There's lots to do and see.
We want to run and splash and laugh
And hunt for shells and snails
And build a castle in the sand
And whisper pirate tales.
We'll look for crabs and pretty rocks
And chase the gulls away.
We have this beach all to ourselves
And we can play all day.

Zolan.

Winter Joys

Snow has fallen on the ground
Very cold and white.
I was sleeping in my bed
As it snowed last night.

I was so excited when
Mommy came to say,
"If we put your snowsuit on,
We'll go out to play."

I was bundled head to toe.
It was cold outside.
"Careful," Daddy said to me,
"Or you'll slip and slide."

I like walking in the snow
With a crunchy noise
I like sleds and snowmen too—
All those winter joys.

Zolan

Baby Ducklings

Here are baby ducklings
Swimming up to me.
They're tiny and they're golden
And they're fluffy, as you see.
They all call out "peep peep peep"
As they paddle by.
I think that's just how baby ducks
Have learned to tell me "Hi."
I really want to touch one,
They are so soft and sweet.
Yet sitting here right close to them
Is such a special treat.
They paddle in the water,
They float like little boats.
All their golden yellow down
Makes perfect duckling coats.
They always swim together,
I count them – there are four.
I wonder, in a moment,
Will they scamper up on shore?
Will they nibble on the grass
And sit right next to me?
That would really make me
As happy as could be.

Zolan.

Brotherly Love

I have a baby brother.
He's very new to me.
I snuggle close to stare at him
And he stares back at me.
He puts his fingers on my cheek.
He looks right in my eyes.
He is a happy little boy.
He hardly ever cries.
I know I'm his big brother
And that he counts on me.
When he's old enough to walk
I'll show him all I see.
We'll always be together
Through sad and happy years.
I'll laugh with him and cry with him
And wipe away his tears.
He seems to sense this all right now
Although he's very young.
He seems to know that I'll stay close.
Our love has just begun.